2 Describe fully each of the numbered and bracketed melodic intervals (e.g. major

J. S. Bach, Cello Suit

Intervals:

1 ....

2 ....

3 ....

4 ....

5 ....

3 These are the actual sounds made by a clarinet in B♭. Rewrite the passage as it would  appear for the player to read, that is, transpose it *up* a major 2nd. Remember to put in the new key signature and add any necessary accidentals.

Reger, *Eine vaterländische Ouvertüre*, Op. 140

4 Look at this extract, which is from *Ballade* for flute and piano by Reinecke, and then answer the questions that follow.

(a) (i) **Mark clearly on the music**, using the appropriate capital letter for identification, one example of each of the following. Also give the bar number of each of your answers, as shown in the answer to **A**.

In bars 1–5

    A a tie in the flute part (circle the notes concerned).   Bar ....2....

    B in the flute part, a dominant note in the
        key of D minor (circle the note concerned).   Bar .... (2)

    C in the piano part, a tonic chord of D minor in
        first inversion (Ib) (circle the notes concerned).   Bar .... (2)

    D in the flute part, a melodic interval of an
        augmented 2nd (circle the notes concerned).   Bar .... (2)

(ii) Rewrite the first right-hand piano chord of the extract so that it sounds at the same pitch, but using the tenor C clef. Remember to put in the clef and the key signature.

(4)

(b) (i) Give the meaning of:

    Adagio   .... (2)

    dolce   .... (2)

    sf (flute, bar 3)   .... (2)

(ii) Name the ornament in the flute part of bar 6.   .... (2)

(iii) Describe the time signature as: simple or compound   .... (1)

                                     duple, triple or quadruple   .... (1)

(c) (i) Write as a breve (double whole-note) an enharmonic equivalent of the last flute note of the extract.

(2)

(ii) Answer TRUE or FALSE to each of the following statements:

The sign above the last flute note of the
extract (>) tells the player to get gradually quieter.   .... (2)

The notes marked ⌐   ⌐ in bars 6–7 of
the flute part form the descending scale of D melodic minor.   .... (2)

(iii) The flute is a member of the woodwind family of orchestral instruments. Name a *different* family of standard orchestral instruments and state its lowest-sounding member.

    Family   ....   Instrument   .... (4)

5 (a) Using semibreves (whole notes), write one octave **ascending** of the **harmonic** minor scale that begins on the given note. Do *not* use a key signature but put in all necessary sharp or flat signs.

(b) Write one octave **descending** of the major scale that has the given key signature. Use semibreves (whole notes) and begin on the tonic.

(a) Compose a complete melody for unaccompanied clarinet or violin, using the given opening. **Indicate the tempo and other performance directions**, including any that might be particularly required for the instrument chosen. The complete melody should be eight bars long.

Instrument for which the melody is written: ....

OR

(b) Compose a complete melody to the following words for a solo voice. Write each syllable under the note or notes to which it is to be sung. Also **indicate the tempo and other performance directions as appropriate**.

> The leaves of the winter wither
> And sink in the forest mould.

Alfred Noyes

Reproduced by kind permission of The Society of Authors as the Literary Representative of the Estate of Alfred Noyes.

7

7 Suggest suitable progressions for two cadences in the following melody by indicating ONLY ONE chord (I, II, IV or V) at each of the places marked A–E. You do not have to indicate the position of the chords, or to state which note is in the bass.

10

Show the chords:

EITHER (a) by writing I, II etc. or any other recognized symbols on the dotted lines below;

OR (b) by writing notes on the staves.

FIRST CADENCE:

Chord A ....

Chord B ....

Chord C ....

SECOND CADENCE:

Chord D ....

Chord E ....

BLANK PAGE

Theory Paper   Grade 5   2014   B

Duration 2 hours

TOTAL MARKS
100

This paper contains SEVEN questions, ALL of which should be answered.
Write your answers on this paper – no others will be accepted.
Answers must be written clearly and neatly – otherwise marks may be lost.

1 (a) Look at the following extract and then answer the questions below.

15

Andante con moto

Alan Belkin, Violin Sonata

(i)   The extract begins on the first beat of the bar and contains some changes of time signature.
Put in the correct time signatures at the three places marked ∗.   (6)

(ii)   Add the correct rest(s) to complete the last bar.   (2)

(b) Look at the following extract and then answer the questions below.

J. S. Bach, Adagio in G major, BWV 968 (adapted)

etc.

(i)   The extract begins on the first beat of the bar. Put in the missing bar-lines.   (3)

(ii)   Name the two ornaments marked **A** and **B**.

A ....   (2)

B ....   (2)

2 Describe fully each of the numbered and bracketed melodic intervals (e.g. minor 2nd). [10]

Reger, Prelude and Fugue in E minor, Op. 117 No. 3

etc.

Intervals:

1 ....

2 ....

3 ....

4 ....

5 ....

3 These are the actual sounds made by a horn in F. Rewrite the passage as it would appear [10]
for the player to read, that is, transpose it *up* a perfect 5th. Do *not* use a key signature but
remember to put in all necessary sharp, flat or natural signs.

d'Indy, *Chanson et danses*, Op. 50 (adapted)

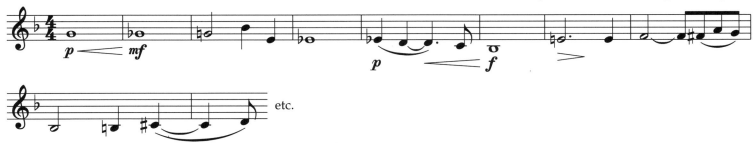

etc.

4 Look at this extract, which is from a song by Schubert, and then answer the questions that follow.

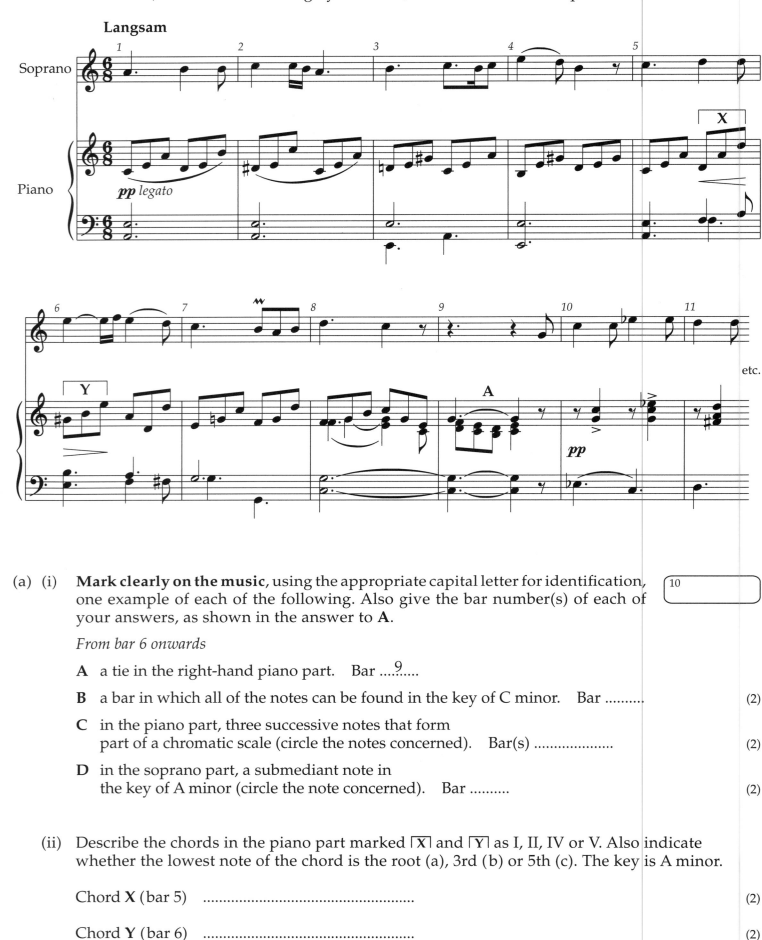

(a) (i) **Mark clearly on the music**, using the appropriate capital letter for identification, one example of each of the following. Also give the bar number(s) of each of your answers, as shown in the answer to **A**.

〔10〕

From bar 6 onwards

A a tie in the right-hand piano part. Bar .....9.....

B a bar in which all of the notes can be found in the key of C minor. Bar .... (2)

C in the piano part, three successive notes that form part of a chromatic scale (circle the notes concerned). Bar(s) .... (2)

D in the soprano part, a submediant note in the key of A minor (circle the note concerned). Bar .... (2)

(ii) Describe the chords in the piano part marked ⌐X⌐ and ⌐Y⌐ as I, II, IV or V. Also indicate whether the lowest note of the chord is the root (a), 3rd (b) or 5th (c). The key is A minor.

Chord **X** (bar 5) .... (2)

Chord **Y** (bar 6) .... (2)

(b) (i) Give the meaning of:

Langsam .... (2)

> (piano, bar 10) .... (2)

(ii) Rewrite the last left-hand note of the extract so that it sounds at the same pitch, but using the tenor C clef. Remember to put in the clef sign.

(2)

(iii) Describe the time signature as: simple or compound .... (1)

duple, triple or quadruple .... (1)

(iv) Write as a breve (double whole-note) an enharmonic equivalent of the second soprano note of the extract.

(2)

(c) (i) The extract is from a song written for soprano, which is the highest-sounding voice. Give the name of the voice part which lies between soprano and alto in vocal range.

.... (2)

(ii) Name a standard orchestral instrument that could play the soprano part of the extract so that it sounds at the same pitch, and state the family of instruments to which it belongs.

Instrument .... Family .... (4)

(iii) Now name a *different* family of standard orchestral instruments and state its lowest-sounding member.

Family .... Instrument .... (4)

13

5 (a) Write the key signature of five flats and then one octave **descending** of the major scale [10] with that key signature. Use semibreves (whole notes) and begin on the tonic.

(b) Write one octave **ascending** of the scale of C♯ **melodic** minor. Do *not* use a key signature but put in all necessary sharp or flat signs. Use semibreves (whole notes) and begin on the tonic.

(a) Compose a complete melody for unaccompanied flute or trumpet, using the given opening. **Indicate the tempo and other performance directions**, including any that might be particularly required for the instrument chosen. The complete melody should be eight bars long.

Instrument for which the melody is written: ....

OR

(b) Compose a complete melody to the following words for a solo voice. Write each syllable under the note or notes to which it is to be sung. Also **indicate the tempo and other performance directions as appropriate**.

> Through all the pleasant meadow-side
> The grass grew shoulder-high.   *Robert Louis Stevenson*

7 Suggest suitable progressions for two cadences in the following melody by indicating ONLY ONE chord (I, II, IV or V) at each of the places marked A–E. You do not have to indicate the position of the chords, or to state which note is in the bass.

Show the chords:

EITHER (a) by writing I, II etc. or any other recognized symbols on the dotted lines below;

OR (b) by writing notes on the staves.

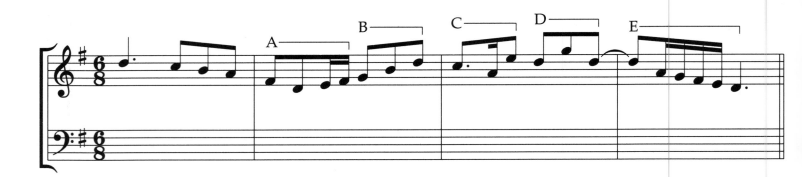

FIRST CADENCE:

SECOND CADENCE:

Chord C ....

Chord A ....

Chord D ....

Chord B ....

Chord E ....

16

BLANK PAGE

Theory Paper   Grade 5   2014   C

Duration 2 hours

This paper contains SEVEN questions, ALL of which should be answered.
Write your answers on this paper – no others will be accepted.
Answers must be written clearly and neatly – otherwise marks may be lost.

TOTAL MARKS
100

1 (a) Look at the following extract and then answer the questions below.

15

Moderato

C. P. E. Bach, Sonata No. 1, H. 30 (adapted)

(i)   The extract begins on the first beat of the bar. Put in the missing bar-lines.   (3)

(ii)   Draw a circle around two notes next to each other that are an augmented 2nd apart.   (2)

(b) Look at the following extract and then answer the questions below.

Clementi, Piano Sonata, Op. 13 No. 6

(i)   Rewrite the extract with the notes correctly grouped (beamed).   (6)

(ii)   Give the time name (e.g. crotchet or quarter note) of the *shortest* note in the extract.

....   (2)

(iii) Write as a breve (double whole-note) an enharmonic equivalent of the first note of the extract.

(2)

18

2 This passage is for SATB choir, written in short score. Rewrite it in open score.

John Bennet, *I languish to complain me* (adapted)

3 Look at this extract, which is adapted from a piano piece by Gurlitt, and then answer the questions that follow.

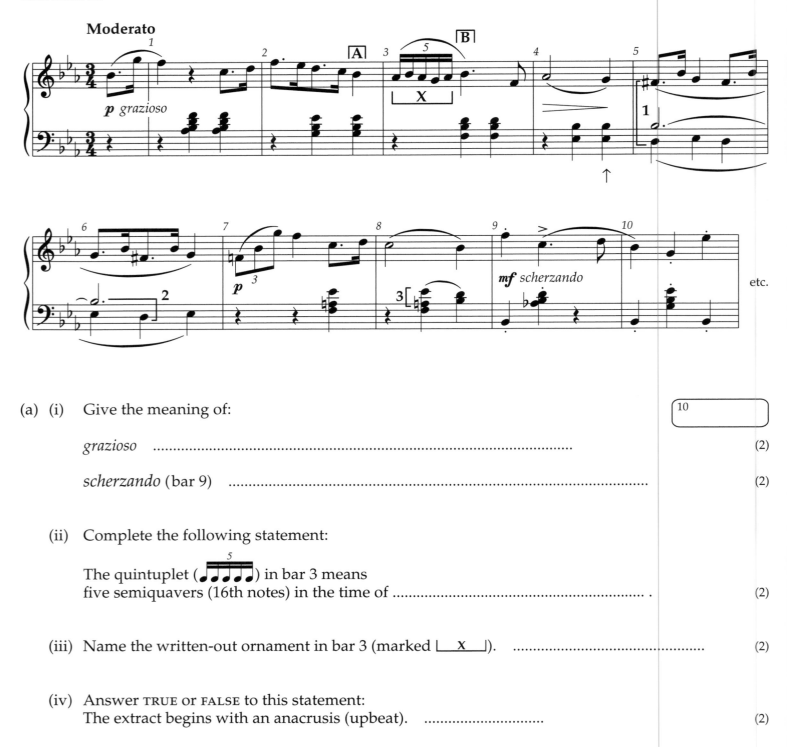

(a) (i) Give the meaning of:

grazioso   ....   (2)

scherzando (bar 9)   ....   (2)

(ii) Complete the following statement:

The quintuplet (♩♩♩♩♩) in bar 3 means
five semiquavers (16th notes) in the time of ....   (2)

(iii) Name the written-out ornament in bar 3 (marked └── X ──┘).   ....   (2)

(iv) Answer TRUE or FALSE to this statement:
The extract begins with an anacrusis (upbeat).   ....   (2)

(b) (i) Describe the chords marked ⌐A⌐ and ⌐B⌐ as I, II, IV or V. Also indicate whether the lowest note of the chord is the root (a), 3rd (b) or 5th (c). The key is E♭ major.

⎧ 10 ⎫

Chord **A** (bar 2)   ....   (2)

Chord **B** (bar 3)   ....   (2)

(ii) Describe fully each of the numbered and bracketed harmonic intervals (e.g. major 2nd).

1 (bar 5, right hand and bottom left-hand)   ....   (2)

2 (bar 6, top and bottom left-hand)   ....   (2)

3 (bar 8, top and middle left-hand)   ....   (2)

(c) (i) Rewrite the last left-hand chord of bar 4 (marked ↑) so that it sounds at the same pitch, but using the tenor C clef. Remember to put in the clef and the key signature.

⎧ 10 ⎫

(4)

(ii) Name a standard orchestral instrument that could play the right-hand part of the extract so that it sounds at the same pitch, and state the family of instruments to which it belongs.

Instrument   ....   Family   ....   (4)

(iii) Now state whether the instrument you named above is a transposing or non-transposing instrument.   ....   (2)

21

4 (a) Put sharps or flats in front of the notes that need them to form the scale of F♯ **melodic** minor. Do *not* use a key signature.

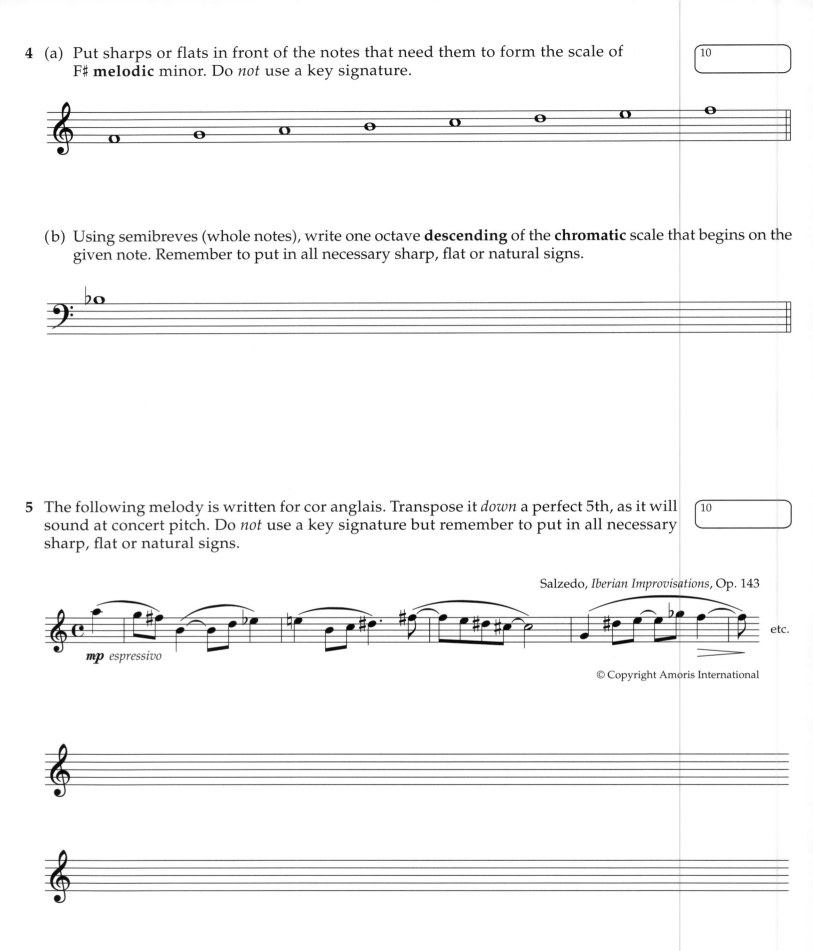

(b) Using semibreves (whole notes), write one octave **descending** of the **chromatic** scale that begins on the given note. Remember to put in all necessary sharp, flat or natural signs.

5 The following melody is written for cor anglais. Transpose it *down* a perfect 5th, as it will sound at concert pitch. Do *not* use a key signature but remember to put in all necessary sharp, flat or natural signs.

Salzedo, *Iberian Improvisations*, Op. 143

mp espressivo

etc.

6 EITHER

15

(a) Compose a complete melody for unaccompanied cello or bassoon, using the given opening. **Indicate the tempo and other performance directions**, including any that might be particularly required for the instrument chosen. The complete melody should be eight bars long.

Instrument for which the melody is written: ....

OR

(b) Compose a complete melody to the following words for a solo voice. Write each syllable under the note or notes to which it is to be sung. Also **indicate the tempo and other performance directions as appropriate**.

> Then away they go to an island fair
> That lies in a Southern sea.   *W. S. Gilbert*

7 Suggest suitable progressions for two cadences in the following melody by indicating **ONLY ONE** chord (I, II, IV or V) at each of the places marked A–E. You do not have to indicate the position of the chords, or to state which note is in the bass.

Show the chords:

EITHER (a) by writing I, II etc. or any other recognized symbols on the dotted lines below;

OR (b) by writing notes on the staves.

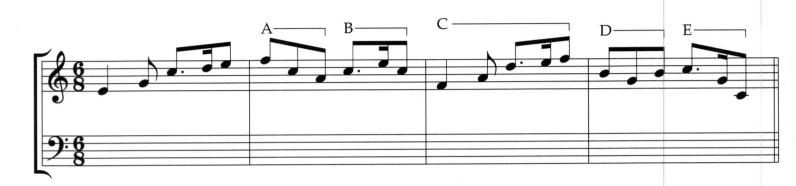

FIRST CADENCE:

Chord A ....

Chord B ....

SECOND CADENCE:

Chord C ....

Chord D ....

Chord E ....

BLANK PAGE

Theory Paper   Grade 5   2014   S

TOTAL MARKS
100

Duration 2 hours

This paper contains SEVEN questions, ALL of which should be answered.
Write your answers on this paper – no others will be accepted.
Answers must be written clearly and neatly – otherwise marks may be lost.

15

1   Look at the following extract, which is for cello, and then answer the questions below.

Allegretto ma non troppo

Glière, *12 Album Leaves*, Op. 51

(a)   The extract begins on the first beat of the bar. Put in the correct time signature.   (2)

(b)   Give the meaning of:

Allegretto ma non troppo   ....   (4)

V (bar 4)   ....   (2)

(c)   Name the ornament in bar 2.   ....   (2)

(d)   Rewrite the first two notes of the extract so that they sound at the same pitch, but using the tenor C clef. Remember to put in the key signature.

(3)

(e)   Complete the following statement:

All the notes in bar 3 can be found in the scale of .... minor.   (2)

2 Describe fully each of the numbered and bracketed melodic intervals (e.g. major 2nd). 10

Rode, 12 Études

Intervals:

1 ....

2 ....

3 ....

4 ....

5 ....

3 These are the actual sounds made by a trumpet in B♭. Rewrite the passage as it would appear for the player to read, that is, transpose it *up* a major 2nd. Remember to put in the new key signature and add any necessary accidentals. 10

Lecail, Concertino for trumpet and piano

4 Look at this extract, which is from a piece for clarinet (written here at concert pitch) and piano by Hurlstone, and then answer the questions that follow.

(a) (i) Give the meaning of:

         10

        Vivace .... (2)

        leggiero (piano, bar 1) .... (2)

        ⁝ (e.g. piano, bar 5) .... (2)

        > (e.g. clarinet, bar 7) .... (2)

   (ii) The triplet (♪♪♪) in the clarinet part in bar 4

        means three semiquavers (16th notes) in the time of .... (2)

(b) (i) Give the letter name of the *highest* note
in the right-hand piano part of the extract. ....

(2)

(ii) Give the time name (e.g. crotchet or
quarter note) of the *shortest* note in the extract. ....

(2)

(iii) Rewrite the first left-hand piano chord of bar 7 (marked ↑) so that it sounds at the
same pitch, but using the alto C clef. Remember to put in the clef and the key signature.

(4)

(iv) The extract begins in the key of B♭ major. In which key does it end? ....

(2)

(c) (i) Give the technical names (e.g. tonic, dominant) of the two notes in the
right-hand piano part marked **A** and **B**. Remember that the key is B♭ major.

10

A (bar 3) ....

(2)

B (bar 4) ....

(2)

(ii) Complete the following statement:

The clarinet is a member of the .... family of orchestral instruments.

(2)

(iii) Now name a *different* family of standard orchestral instruments and state its
lowest-sounding member.

Family .... Instrument ....

(4)

5 (a) Using semibreves (whole notes), write one octave **ascending** of the **melodic** minor
scale that begins on the given note. Do *not* use a key signature but put in all necessary
sharp or flat signs.

(b) Write the key signature of four sharps and then one octave **descending** of the major scale with that
key signature. Use semibreves (whole notes) and begin on the tonic.

(a) Compose a complete melody for unaccompanied bassoon or cello, using the given opening. **Indicate the tempo and other performance directions**, including any that might be particularly required for the instrument chosen. The complete melody should be eight bars long.

Instrument for which the melody is written: ....

OR

(b) Compose a complete melody to the following words for a solo voice. Write each syllable under the note or notes to which it is to be sung. Also **indicate the tempo and other performance directions as appropriate**.

> Along the sea-sands damp and brown
> The traveller hastens toward the town.
>   *H. W. Longfellow*

7 Suggest suitable progressions for two cadences in the following melody by indicating
ONLY ONE chord (I, II, IV or V) at each of the places marked A–E. You do not have to
indicate the position of the chords, or to state which note is in the bass.

Show the chords:

EITHER   (a)   by writing I, II etc. or any other recognized symbols on the dotted lines below;

OR   (b)   by writing notes on the staves.

FIRST CADENCE:

Chord A   ....

Chord B   ....

Chord C   ....

SECOND CADENCE:

Chord D   ....

Chord E   ....

ABRSM
24 Portland Place
London W1B 1LU
United Kingdom

www.abrsm.org

Published by ABRSM (Publishing) Ltd,
a wholly owned subsidiary of ABRSM
Cover by Kate Benjamin & Andy Potts
Printed in England by Halstan & Co. Ltd,
Amersham, Bucks
Reprinted in 2016

ISBN 978-1-84849-724-5